Sticker Atlas
The World

Illustrated by
Garry Fleming

Book 1

The Earth's Landscapes

Mountains

Mountains cover 24 per cent of Earth's surface. The tops of many mountains are so high that they are covered with ice or snow.

Mountains can be created by volcanoes erupting. When molten rock pours up out of the ground it cools to form many of the mountain formations we see today.

Most of Earth's mountains were formed by great earth movements millions of years ago. They are constantly being worn away to form hills, sand on the beaches or soil on the ground.

The highest mountain on Earth is Mount Everest, in Nepal. It is 8848 metres above sea level. That is as high as 23 Empire State Buildings piled on top of each other!

The longest river in the world is the Nile, which runs from Tanzania, in the centre of Africa, to Egypt in the north, and into the Mediterranean Sea. It is 6670 kilometres long.

Volcanoes

Volcanoes are mountains that have an opening in the top, but with lava and gases trapped underneath. When the lava and gases rumble up from below the ground and escape out of the hole at the top of the volcano, it is called an eruption.

There are many active volcanoes around the world, including Mount St Helens in the USA and Mount Etna in Italy. There are also many extinct volcanoes. This means they no longer erupt.

In Italy around 2000 years ago, Mount Vesuvius erupted burying the entire city of Pompeii under rock and ash.

Rivers

Rivers are large, long trenches that carry fresh water from higher ground to lower ground. Rivers are created when large amounts of water continually travel along the same path, cutting deeper and deeper into the ground until a trench is formed.

The water from rivers can come from under the ground, from rain or from melting ice caps on mountains. Most rivers empty into oceans or lakes, but in some very hot, dry areas, the water can just evaporate before it has a chance to make it out to sea.

Oceans

Oceans are enormous bodies of salt water that surround Earth's continents. Oceans cover about 71 per cent of Earth's surface. There are five oceans: the Pacific, Atlantic, Indian, Southern and Arctic.

Oceans are not only very large, but are also very deep. Out in the middle of the ocean, the bottom is so far down that no light reaches there. Many strange creatures live in this part of the ocean, many of which, it is believed, have not been discovered yet as the water is too deep for humans to explore. The Mariana Trench in the Pacific Ocean has its ocean floor more than 10 kilometres below the surface!

The world's largest ocean is the Pacific, which covers about one third of the Earth's surface.

Lakes

Lakes are large bodies of water surrounded by land. They do not join to the sea like most rivers do.

Lakes are very important to humans and animals alike. Lakes supply many towns and cities with fresh drinking water. Lakes also support a huge amount of plant and animal life, including ducks, frogs and fish.

Over 60 per cent of the world's lakes are in Canada.

Deserts

Deserts are large, dry areas of land that lose more moisture than they gain from rain. Deserts cover about one third of all of the land on Earth.

While deserts are very hot during the day, most deserts get very cold during the night. This is because the air is so dry that it cannot block out the sun's heat during the day, or hold on to the warmth in the air at night.

Deserts are usually great areas of sand or rock with very little plant life.

The whole of Australia could fit inside the Sahara desert in Africa!

Environmental Issues

Air pollution

Air pollution occurs when gases and chemicals created by humans are released into the atmosphere. Some of these chemicals then eat away at the ozone layer, which is the part of Earth's atmosphere that protects us from harsh rays of the sun.

The only way to stop air pollution is for governments, businesses and people at home to try really hard to reduce the amount of pollutants released into the air.

Water pollution

Water pollution occurs when people dump their waste into the sea. Water pollution has a terrible effect on sea life, as it can make their home too dirty to live in. Water pollution also kills coral reefs, which are the sea's natural gardens.

Global warming

The world's average temperature has increased very slightly over the last 100 years. This is known as global warming. Many scientists believe that humans have had such a bad impact on the planet that it is actually us making the world get warmer.

Even a slight change in temperature can have a big impact on our planet. It can cause drought, melt ice caps on mountains and raise sea levels, all of which can affect humans, plant-life and animals.

Resource depletion

When people from a certain country or region of the world use more natural resources than they can replace, it is known as resource depletion. Some of the main causes of resource depletion are mining, fishing, deforestation and drilling and digging for fossil fuels, such as oil and coal.

Resource depletion can have a bad effect on the environment because, as the resources become scarce, people have to go to greater lengths to extract the resources they need from the land.

Overpopulation

Everybody needs resources such as food, drinking water and materials to make shelter, in order to survive. Overpopulation is what happens when there are not enough resources in a certain area to support the number of people living there.

Soil erosion

Erosion is what occurs when the nutrient-rich top layer of the land's soil is washed away by water or carried away in the wind. When this happens, it can make the soil unsuitable for growing crops. The major causes of soil erosion are deforestation, overfarming and overgrazing.

The Continents
Africa

Africa is the world's second largest continent. It is made up of many different nations that each have their own unique and colourful culture. Some of the main languages spoken in Africa are Swahili, Arabic and English.

Africa is considered by many scientists to be the oldest inhabited continent on Earth, which means people lived there before they lived anywhere else.

Africa's landscape is made up of tropical jungle and grassy plains in the south and hot, dry deserts in the north. In fact, Africa is home to the world's largest and hottest desert, the Sahara.

Population: 900 000 000
Largest country: Sudan
Longest river: The Nile
Highest mountain: Mount Kilimanjaro
in Tanzania

■ Africa

Antarctica

Antarctica is a gigantic frozen continent which covers the very bottom part of the earth. There are no native people in Antarctica – the only people who live there are researchers who visit from many different countries around the world. Antarctica has been divided up into a number of different 'claims' (areas that are looked after by a certain country). The largest portion has been claimed by Australia.

Antarctica is the coldest and windiest place on Earth. Even though 98 per cent of Antarctica is covered in ice, and around 70 per cent of all the fresh water on Earth is held in that ice, it is also the world's driest continent. It hardly ever rains in Antarctica!

Population: 1000 to 4000 (but none permanent)
Largest territory: Australian Antarctic Territory
Longest river: The Onyx
Highest mountain: Mount Vinson Massif

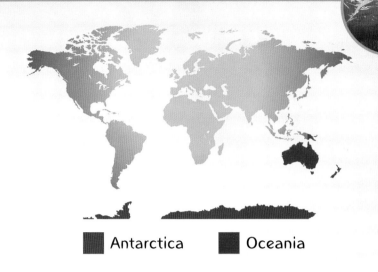

■ Antarctica   ■ Oceania

Oceania

Oceania is the world's smallest and least populated continent. It is made up of Australia, the world's largest island, as well as a number of other island countries including New Zealand and New Guinea. This continent is also sometimes called Australasia.

The first people were thought to have arrived in Australia from southern Asia around 50 000 years ago, and a few thousand years later, some travelled to New Zealand and other Australasian islands.

Around one third of Australia is made up of hot, dry deserts, while New Zealand is very mountainous, and the surrounding islands, including New Guinea, are covered with thick, tropical jungle.

Population: 33 000 000
Largest country: Australia
Longest river: The Murray–Darling
Highest mountain: Mount Wilhelm in
Papua New Guinea

Asia

Asia is the world's largest continent. It is also the continent with the most people living on it – in fact, six out of every ten people in the world live in Asia!

Asia is home to the Chinese and Japanese civilisations – some of the oldest in the world. Some interesting inventions that originated in Asia are paper, the compass and kites.

The top part of Asia, made up mostly of Russia, is cold and icy. The bottom part is made up of dense jungle and rainforest, while the central and western areas contain large deserts.

Population: 4 000 000 000
Largest country: China
Longest river: The Yangtze
Highest mountain: Mount Everest in Nepal

■ Asia

The Great Wall of China is around 6700 kilometres long – that's one and a half times the width of Australia!

The Himalaya Range of Asia is the world's largest mountain system. The Himalayas include eight out of the ten highest peaks in the world.

Europe

Europe is the world's second smallest continent. It is home to many of the world's most famous cities, including London, Paris, Rome and Berlin.

Some of history's most famous civilisations began in Europe, such as the Ancient Greeks and the Roman Empire. Europe has also produced many famous artists, such as Vincent Van Gough, Pablo Picasso and Leonardo da Vinci.

Europe contains the world's largest country, Russia. This country is so big that it actually sits across two continents, Europe and Asia.

■ Europe

Population: 728 000 000
Largest country: Russia (also partly in Asia)
Longest river: The Volga
Highest mountain: Mount Elbrus in Russia

Europe is also home to the world's smallest country, the Vatican City. A small territory within the borders of Italy, the Vatican City is the home of the leader of the Catholic church, the Pope.

The climate in the north of Europe is cold and icy, while in the south it is sunny and warm.

North America

North America is made up of three very large countries: The United States of America (USA), Canada and Mexico, as well as Greenland and many other smaller nations and islands.

During the last ice ages, North America used to be connected to Asia by a land bridge that ran from the USA state of Alaska to the eastern part of Russia.

The northern parts of the continent are freezing – in parts of Canada the temperature can be as low as minus 40 degrees Celsius. The southern region, including Texas and Mexico, is hot and dry, and much of it is made up of desert.

North America

Population: 524 000 000
Largest country: Canada
Longest river: The Mississippi–Missouri
Highest mountain: Mount McKinley in the USA

South America

South America is the world's fourth largest continent. Over half of the people in South America live in Brazil, its largest country.

Most of the people of South America speak Spanish or Portuguese, but many also speak the traditional languages that existed before European settlement.

South America is home to many amazing natural features, such as the world's highest waterfall, largest river, driest desert, longest mountain range and largest rainforest.

The Amazon rainforest, the world's largest, is home to more plant and animal species than anywhere else on Earth.

South America

Population: 382 000 000
Largest country: Brazil
Longest river: The Amazon
Highest mountain: Mount Aconcagua in Argentina

How to use your giant wall map

The wall map shows each of the world's six inhabited continents. Each continent is placed inside a box so that you can clearly see what countries are part of that continent.

Around the edges of the continents are boxes for you to place the flag stickers into.

The flag stickers have the names of the countries printed under them. Choose a sticker, then look for a box which has that country written below it on the map. Place the sticker in the box, and you're done!

North America

Antigua and Barbuda	Barbados	Belize	Canada	Costa Rica	Cuba	Dominica	Dominican Republic	El Sal	Grenada
Guatemala	Haiti	Honduras	Jamaica	Mexico	Nicaragua	Panama	The Bahamas	Trinida	States of America

The wall map has lots of little pictures, called icons, on each of the continents. Have a look at the icons. Do you recognise them? The icons can tell you about what kinds of people, animals, places or things can be found in that part of the world.

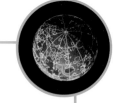

Sticker Atlas
Space

Designed by
Sonia Dixon

Book 2

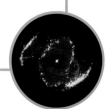

The universe

The word 'universe' refers to everything in all of space and time. The universe is made up of everything that exists. This includes planets, stars and galaxies. Many scientists believe the big bang theory, which states that the universe was created about 13.73 billion years ago due to an explosion called the 'big bang'. Before that, everything in the universe was contained in a hot and dense state called the 'Planck Epoch'. After the big bang, the universe began to expand, and it is still doing so.

The Milky Way is about 100 000 light years in diameter.

Milky Way galaxy

Gravity is when objects of smaller mass are pulled towards objects of larger mass.

The Milky Way

The Milky Way is the name of the galaxy in which our solar system is located. The Milky Way is spiral shaped.

Stars and galaxies

The universe is full of stars. Stars are massive balls of plasma (a kind of hot gas) that are held together by gravity. Planets are objects that orbit (complete a full circle of) a star. The closest star to Earth is the sun, which the earth orbits, along with the other planets in our solar system. The solar system belongs to the Milky Way galaxy, which is a member of a supercluster of galaxies we call the Local Group.

Groups of stars cluster together to form galaxies, and galaxies cluster together to form superclusters.

A supercluster of galaxies

The sun

The sun is one of billions of stars in the Milky Way galaxy and is made of hydrogen and helium gas. Hydrogen gets turned to helium within the sun, producing energy.

The sun is located about 149 600 000 km (92 957 130 mi) from Earth. It supports life on Earth, controlling the climate and weather

The core of the sun is extremely hot, about 15 000 000°C (27 000 000°F); its surface (called the 'photosphere') is al 5500°C (9930°F). sun's corona or ou atmosphere can b during total solar

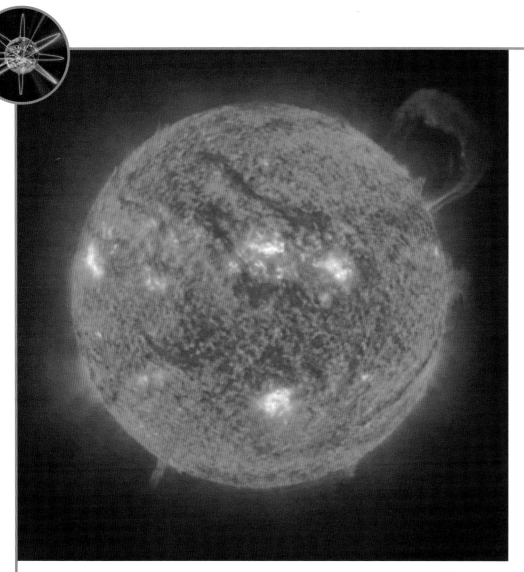

The sun

Even though it is about 1 400 000 times the size of Earth, the sun is a below-average size for a star.

Solar eclipse

A solar eclipse occurs when the moon passes directly between the sun and Earth. A partial eclipse is when the moon covers only part of the s total eclipse is when the moon the sun completely, blocking light.

Total solar eclipse

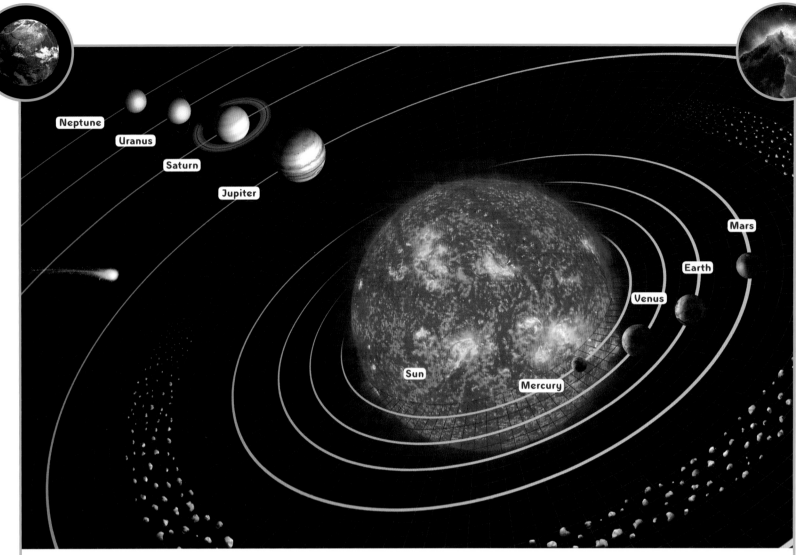

Neptune
Uranus
Saturn
Jupiter
Mars
Earth
Venus
Sun
Mercury

The solar system

A solar system consists of a star (or sometimes two or more stars!) and the objects that orbit it.

Our solar system is thought to have formed about 4.6 billion years ago when a giant molecular cloud collapsed. The centre of the cloud became hot and dense, eventually becoming the sun, our star. Particles of dust then clumped together to form massive boulders, becoming the planets as they are today.

Because the sun is so massive in comparison to the planets, they are drawn into its gravity, which is why the planets are continually orbiting the sun.

There are four smaller planets close to the sun – Mercury, Venus, Earth and Mars. They are mainly made of rock and metal and are called 'terrestrial planets'. An asteroid belt divides the terrestrial planets from the 'gas giants': Jupiter, Saturn, Uranus and Neptune. These planets are massive and made mostly of gases like hydrogen and helium. After the gas giants is the Kuiper Belt.

The planets orbit the sun in an anti-clockwise direction, and their orbits are 'elliptical' (oval-shaped).

Mercury

Mercury is the closest planet to the sun. From Earth, Mercury can be seen best in the morning or at twilight.

Mercury

Mercury has many craters made by meteorites crashing into its surface billions of years ago. The temperature of Mercury ranges from around −180°C to 427°C (−292°F to 800°F). Mercury has a large core made of iron, almost no atmosphere, and no moons.

Venus

Venus

Venus is the second-closest planet to the sun. Viewed from Earth at night, Venus is the brightest object after the moon.

Venus is covered in clouds of sulfuric acid and its atmosphere consists mainly of carbon dioxide. Venus is dusty and dry, and it has constant, extremely hot temperatures (about

When Soviet scientists sent space probes to Venus, they detected constant lightning and thunder. As there is no rain on Venus, this lightning may have been formed by ash from giant volcanic eruptions.

460°C [800°F]), which are a result of the dense carbon atmosphere trapping infrared radiation from the sun. Venus is covered in volcanoes, some of them reaching 100 km (62 mi) across. It has no moons.

Earth

Earth is the third planet from the sun, and the only planet in the solar system that we're sure has liquid water on its surface. This is what enables life to exist on Earth. As far as we know, Earth is the only place in the universe that supports life. The earth's magnetic field and layer of ozone serve to protect life on the surface from harmful radiation and from meteorite bombardment. It takes the earth 365.25 days to orbit the sun.

Earth's core is made mainly of iron. The surface, called the 'crust', is a rocky shell that is divided into large plates.

Earth's magnetic field stretches into space and protects the earth from solar wind – high energy particles that come from the sun.

The United States sent a spaceship to the moon in 1969. Neil Armstrong and Buzz Aldrin were the astronauts who walked on the moon and spent a day on its surface.

The moon

When a planet has a natural satellite (an object that orbits it) we call this a 'moon'. Earth has one moon. The moon makes an orbit around the earth every 27.3 days. There is no air or liquid on the moon's rocky surface. It is marked with many craters left from asteroid collisions.

The reason that the moon seems to change shape from night to night is that its exposure to the sun alters.

Mars

Mars

Mars is the fourth planet from the sun. It is sometimes called the 'Red Planet' because of its colour, which is due to the iron oxide of its surface. Mars has a thin atmosphere and probably a small iron core.

Mars is home to Olympus Mons, the highest known mountain in our solar system, as well as Valles Marineris, the largest canyon. Water ice has been found on Mars, and it is possible that Mars used to have a lot of water on its surface and perhaps life. Mars has two small irregular-shaped moons, Phobos and Deimos.

Mars' moons are probably asteroids that have been captured by its gravity.

Deimos

Phobos

Asteroid belt

Asteroid belt

Between Mars and Jupiter is the asteroid belt. This region of the solar system is full of objects called asteroids. The asteroid belt is also home to Ceres, a large asteroid that has been classified as a dwarf planet. Asteroids were probably formed from fragments of planets that have broken off. When asteroids collide, they make smaller fragments of rock called meteoroids. These sometimes crash into Earth as meteorites.

If a large asteroid collided with the earth's surface, it could cause devastation and temperature change. A large asteroid crashing into the earth may have been the reason that dinosaurs became extinct.

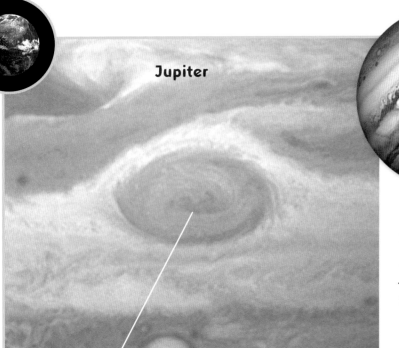

Jupiter

The Great Red Spot

Jupiter

Jupiter is mainly made of hydrogen and helium, probably with a small rocky core. The planet is surrounded by faint planetary rings made of dust.

Jupiter has at least 63 moons, including the Galilean moons that were discovered in 1610 by Galileo Galilei.

Io

Jupiter

Jupiter is the fifth planet from the sun and the largest planet in the solar system. It is a gas giant, and its colourful-looking surface is caused by clouds in its atmosphere made of ammonia, methane and water ice.

Callisto

Ganymede

Europa

The Great Red Spot is a giant storm on Jupiter that has been going for over 300 years. It is larger than two Earths.

Saturn's rings

Saturn

Saturn

Saturn is the sixth planet from the sun and the second-largest planet. This gas giant is composed mainly of hydrogen, with a small core of

rock and ice. Saturn is known for its rings, which are made mainly of ice particles. There are seven major rings and thousands of smaller ringlets.

Saturn has 61 known moons, including Titan, the solar system's second-largest moon after Jupiter's Ganymede.

Saturn's orbit around the sun takes about 29.5 years.

Uranus has faint rings made of black ice.

Uranus

Uranus is the seventh planet from the sun. Unlike Jupiter and Saturn, Uranus and Neptune fit into the category of 'ice giants', as they contain larger amounts of ices. Uranus' atmosphere

Uranus

is made mainly of water, ammonia and methane, making it the coldest planet in the solar system. Its surface has almost no features apart from some fast-moving clouds.

Uranus is tilted, and orbits the sun nearly on its side.

Neptune

Neptune

Neptune is the eighth planet from the sun. It has 11 moons, including Triton, its largest. Neptune is an ice giant made mainly of hydrogen and helium, with an icy, rocky core. The planet's blue appearance is due to the traces of methane in its outer regions. Although Neptune's surface is featureless, it has visible weather patterns and storms.

Unlike any other major moon in the solar system, Neptune's moon Triton orbits in the opposite direction to its parent.

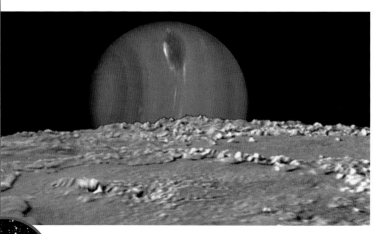

Neptune on Triton's horizon

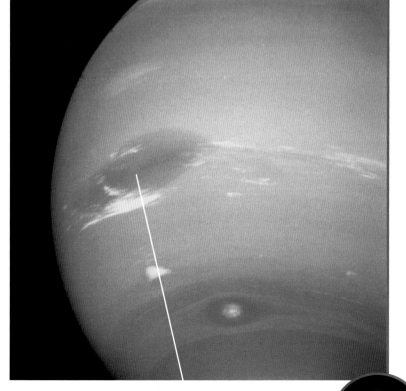

Neptune's Great Dark Spot

Pluto and the Kuiper Belt

Beyond Neptune lies the Kuiper Belt, containing Pluto, the second-largest known dwarf planet in the solar system (after Eris). Pluto used to be classified as a planet, but was reclassified as a dwarf planet in 2006. Pluto's core is most probably rocky with a thin atmosphere of nitrogen and methane. It has a moon called Charon.

Unlike the rocky asteroid belt, the Kuiper Belt objects are mainly made of ice. As well as Pluto, the dwarf planets Haumea and Makemake can be found in the Kuiper Belt.

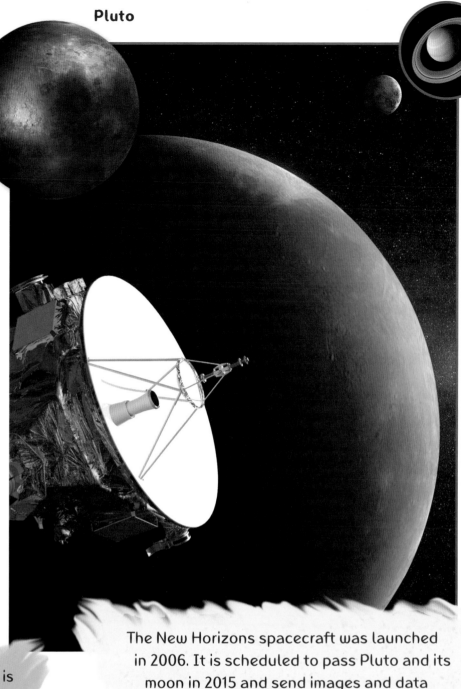

The New Horizons spacecraft was launched in 2006. It is scheduled to pass Pluto and its moon in 2015 and send images and data back to Earth.

Halley's comet is the most famous comet, as it is easily visible to the naked eye and can be seen from Earth every 75 to 76 years. Halley's comet will next appear in mid-2061.

Halley's comet

Comets

Comets are small objects that orbit the sun. When a comet gets close to the sun, the solar radiation affects the comet's nucleus and makes it form a cloud of dust and gas called a 'coma'. This cloud is blown by the solar wind into an enormous tail. The coma and the tail are illuminated by the sun, and can become visible from Earth when the comet passes through the inner solar system.

NASA's twin Exploration Rovers landed on the surface of Mars in 2004. They have been very helpful in providing information about the surface of the 'Red Planet'.

Space exploration

Space exploration involves using technology and astronomy to explore outer space. From Earth, we can see the moon, planets, distant stars and even other galaxies. Telescopes are very useful tools for observing outer space from Earth.

Although people have always been able to observe the sky, humans and robots have only been able to physically explore space since the early 20th century. In 1957, Sputnik 1 was the first man-made object to orbit Earth. The first moon landing took place in 1969. Since then, many manned and unmanned spacecraft have explored space.

The Hubble Space Telescope was launched into orbit by NASA (the USA's National Aeronautics and Space Administration) in 1990 and is an extremely useful tool for observing space.

The International Space Station is a research laboratory being assembled in Low Earth Orbit. It is a joint program of the United States, Russia, Japan, Canada and ten European nations.

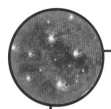

How to use your giant wall chart

The wall chart shows our solar system and the objects that inhabit it, as well as some features of space exploration. On and around the wall chart is space for you to place the stickers that complete these images.

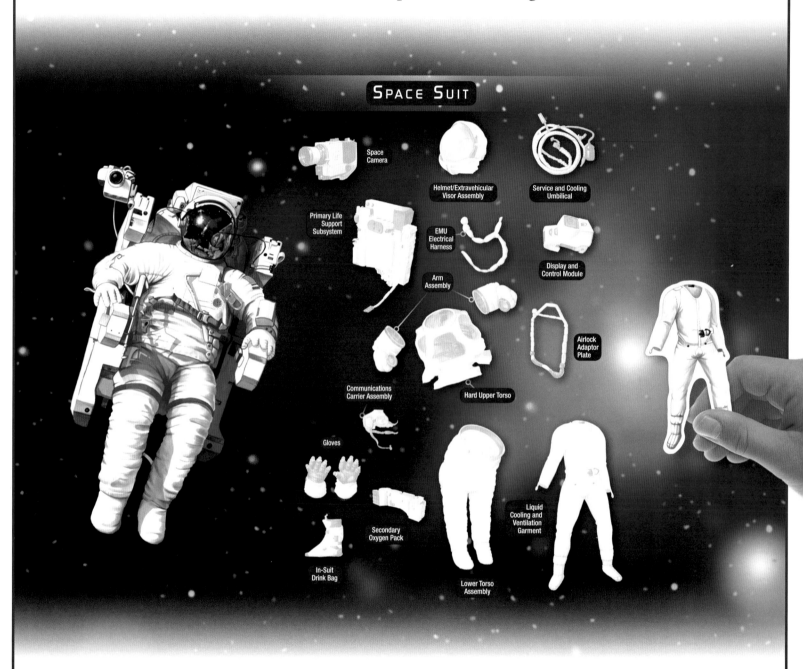

SPACE SUIT

Space Camera

Helmet/Extravehicular Visor Assembly

Service and Cooling Umbilical

Primary Life Support Subsystem

EMU Electrical Harness

Display and Control Module

Arm Assembly

Airlock Adaptor Plate

Communications Carrier Assembly

Hard Upper Torso

Gloves

Liquid Cooling and Ventilation Garment

Secondary Oxygen Pack

In-Suit Drink Bag

Lower Torso Assembly

The stickers have labels printed under them. Choose a sticker, then look for a picture that matches that sticker on the chart. Place the sticker over the picture and you're done!

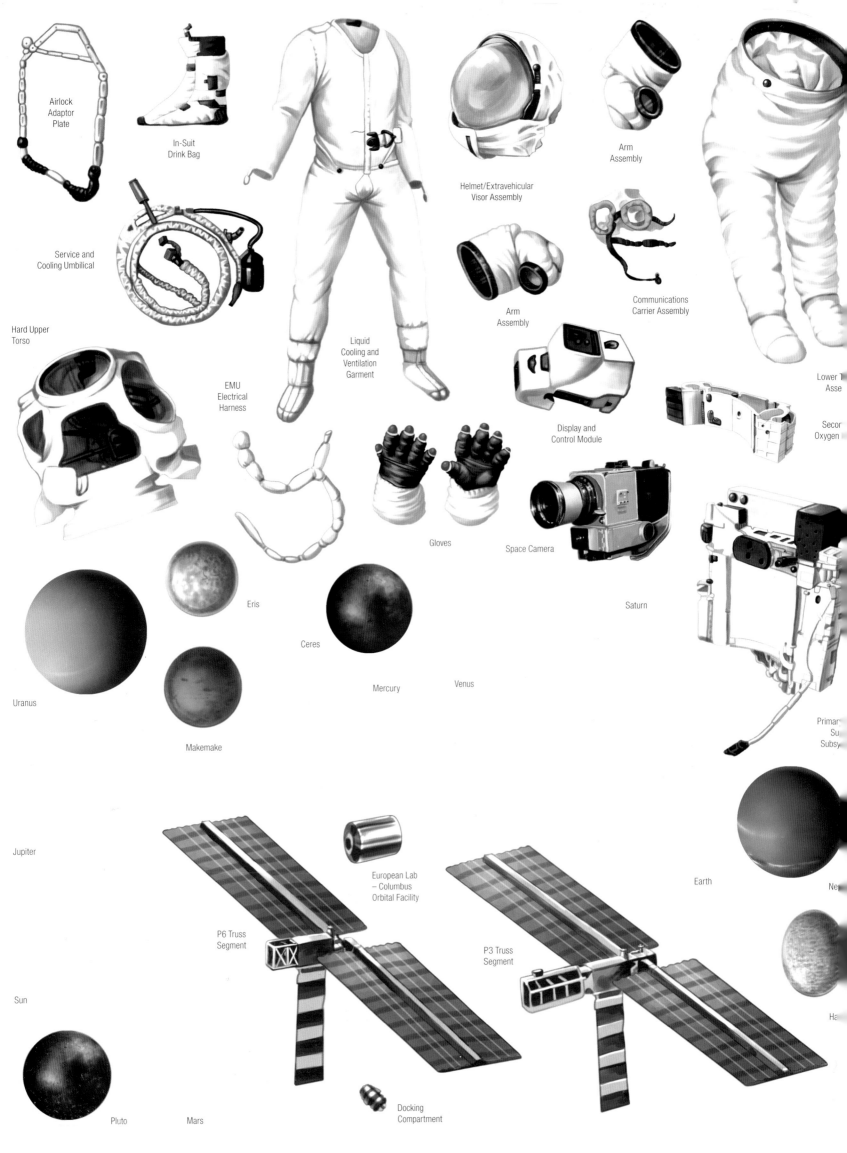

Airlock
Adaptor
Plate

In-Suit
Drink Bag

Helmet/Extravehicular
Visor Assembly

Arm
Assembly

Service and
Cooling Umbilical

Communications
Carrier Assembly

Hard Upper
Torso

Arm
Assembly

Liquid
Cooling and
Ventilation
Garment

EMU
Electrical
Harness

Lower T
Asse

Secor
Oxygen

Display and
Control Module

Gloves

Space Camera

Saturn

Eris

Ceres

Mercury

Venus

Uranus

Primar
Su
Subsy

Makemake

Jupiter

European Lab
– Columbus
Orbital Facility

Earth

Ne

P6 Truss
Segment

P3 Truss
Segment

Sun

Ha

Pluto

Mars

Docking
Compartment

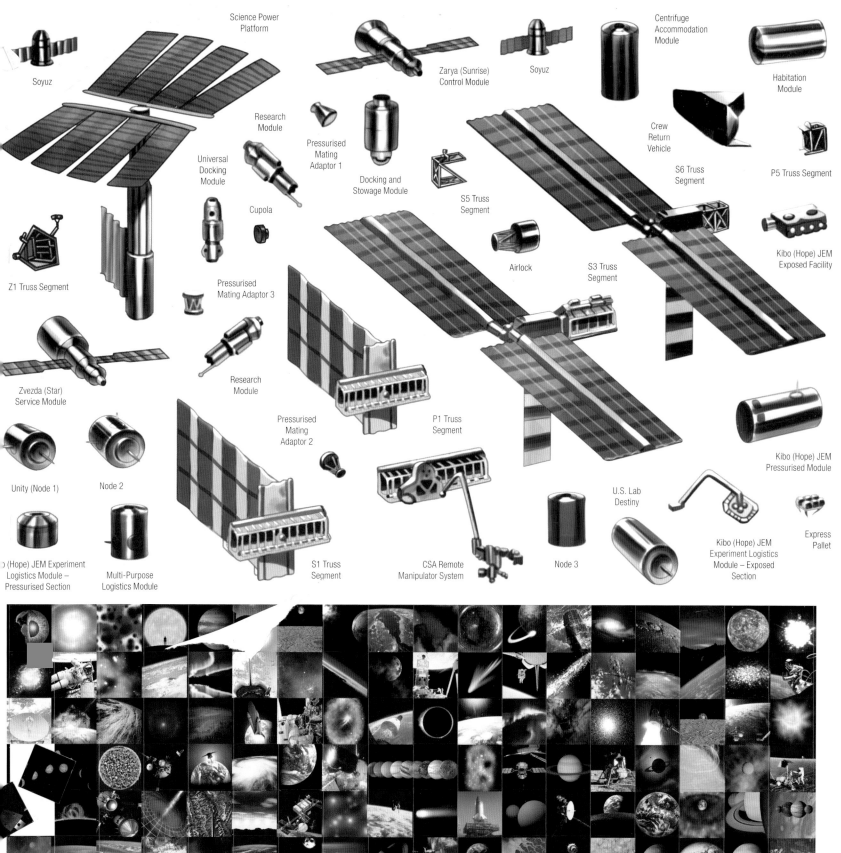

Soyuz

Science Power Platform

Zarya (Sunrise) Control Module

Soyuz

Centrifuge Accommodation Module

Habitation Module

Research Module

Pressurised Mating Adaptor 1

Crew Return Vehicle

S6 Truss Segment

P5 Truss Segment

Universal Docking Module

Docking and Stowage Module

Cupola

S5 Truss Segment

Airlock

S3 Truss Segment

Kibo (Hope) JEM Exposed Facility

Z1 Truss Segment

Pressurised Mating Adaptor 3

Research Module

Pressurised Mating Adaptor 2

P1 Truss Segment

Zvezda (Star) Service Module

Kibo (Hope) JEM Pressurised Module

Unity (Node 1)

Node 2

S1 Truss Segment

CSA Remote Manipulator System

Node 3

U.S. Lab Destiny

Express Pallet

o (Hope) JEM Experiment Logistics Module – Pressurised Section

Multi-Purpose Logistics Module

Kibo (Hope) JEM Experiment Logistics Module – Exposed Section